Dear Grandma

from you to me®

from you to me®

GIFTS THAT TOUCH LIVES

Dear Grandma

from you to me®

This book is for your Grandmother's unique and amazing story.

It is for her to capture some of her life's key memories, experiences and feelings.

Ask her to complete it carefully and, if she wants to, add some photographs or images to personalise it more.

When it is finished and returned to you, this will be a record of her story . . . a story that you will treasure forever.

Dear Nana,

Here is my letter to you ...

I would like you to help me fill out this book all about you, your life and memories so that I can keep forever ☺

Lots of love

Kirsteen
xxx

Tell me about the time and place you were born . . .

What are your earliest memories?

I'd like to know about your parents . . . names, dates of birth and tell me some stories about them . . .

Tell me what you know about your Mother's parents and family . . .

Tell me what you know about your Father's parents and family . . .

Please detail what you know of our family tree . . .

What **interesting** information do you know about other people in our family?

Here's some space for you to add more about our family that will **interest** generations to come . . .

What do you remember about the place/s you lived when you were a child?

What were your favourite childhood toys or games?

What sort of pets did you have when you were young and what were their names?

What do you remember about your holidays
as a child?

What did you do for entertainment when you were young?

What did you study at school and what were you best at?

Tell me about the things you did as a child that are different for today's children . . .

What did you want to do when you grew up?

What were your favourite hobbies when you were young?

Did you have an idol when you were young?
Tell me who and why . . .

What was the first piece of music you bought?

What chores had to be done when you were young that aren't needed to be done today?

Describe any family traditions you had
or maybe still have . . .

What age were you when you started work?
Tell me about the jobs you have had . . .

How did you meet my Grandfather?

What would you do for a **night-out** when you were dating?

Tell me about a memorable piece of music that you and my Grandfather had 'just for you' . . .

Describe a special day you had with my Grandfather . . .

Choosing the names for your children can be really difficult . . . how did you decide?

I would love to know more about my parents
. . . what can you tell me?

Tell me what my Mum / Dad was like
when they were younger . . .

How did you feel when you were told you were going to be a grandparent?

What did you think when you first saw me after I was born?

Can you see any characteristics in me that come from other people in our family?

In what ways am I similar or different to my Mum / Dad?

Describe some of your favourite memories of the times we have spent together . . .

Describe what you like about me . . .

Is there anything you would like to change
about me?

Tell me about the friends you have had in your life . . .

Yellow
Submarine

What piece/s of music would you choose in your own favourite 'top 10'?

Tell me about the most interesting places you have travelled to . . .

What are the happiest or greatest memories of your life?

What are a few of your favourite things?

Describe your memory of some major world events that have happened in your lifetime . . .

Describe the greatest change that you have seen in your lifetime so far . . .

Do you think life today is better or worse than when you were young? How is it different?

Who or what has been the greatest influence on you?

If you were an animal . . . what type of animal would you be, and why?

If you won the Lottery . . . what would you do with the money?

What have you found most difficult in your life?

What is your biggest regret in your life?

Can you do anything about it now?

Tell me about the things that have made you happy or laugh . . .

With hindsight what would you do differently?

Describe something you still want to **achieve** in your life . . .

Tell me something you think I won't know about you . . .

What would you like your epitaph to say?

Given your experiences, what advice would you like to offer me?

And now your chance to tell me some other **personal stories** that you want to share . . .

These extra pages are for us to write any
questions, memories or answers that
may not have been covered elsewhere in the book . . .

And finally for the record . . .

what is your full name ?

what was your maiden name ?

what is your date of birth ?

what colour are your eyes ?

how tall are you ?

what blood group are you ?

what was the date when you completed this story for me ?

And a few words to thank you for completing this Journal of a Lifetime ...

Published by from you to me ltd

All titles are available from good gift and book shops or www.fromyoutome.com

from you to me **Journals of a Lifetime**

Dear Mum
Dear Dad
Dear Grandma
Dear Grandad
Dear Sister
Dear Brother
Dear Daughter
Dear Son
Dear Friend

You can also use this code
by downloading a free QR
code reader app to your
smart phone.

Parent & Child

Bump to Birthday, pregnancy & first year journal
Our Story, for my daughter
Our Story, for my son
Mum to Mum - pass it on
Dear Baby, guest book

Teen & Tween

Mum & Me
Dad & Me
Rant & Rave - My School
Rant & Rave - My Holiday

Other Titles

Love Stories, anniversary & relationship journal
Cooking up Memories
Digging up Memories
Kicking off Memories
Dear Future Me
These were the Days
Christmas Present, Christmas Past

Personalised

Many of these journals can be personalised online at www.fromyoutome.com

Dear Grandma

from you to me®

First published in the UK by from you to me, August 2007
Copyright, from you to me limited 2007
Re-designed in January 2012
Hackless House, Murhill, Bath, BA2 7FH
www.fromyoutome.com
E-mail: hello@fromyoutome.com

ISBN 978-1-907048-46-3

Cover design by so design consultants www.so-design.co.uk

This book is printed on woodfree paper produced from a sustainable source and Elemental Chlorine Free paper sourced to FSC standards. Printed in India by Replika Press on behalf of JFDI print services Ltd.

If you think other questions should be included in future editions, please let us know. And please share some of the interesting answers you receive with us at the *from you to me* website to let other people read about these fascinating insights . . .